A Day to Remember

Have you ever had a day to remember,
Like the day of the seven-inch snow in November?

The day you fed the lonely, stray kitten you found;
Or rode the big golden horse on the merry-go-round;

Slept all night in your tent or climbed your first tree;
Ran in the sand when you first saw the sea;

Took a trip to the dentist, had a ride on a train;
Or just held your dad's hand as you walked in the rain?

Such a day can take place at home or away.
A day to remember can be every day.

~ Jan Joss

Reading *1D* **Third Edition**

bju press®

Greenville, South Carolina

NOTE:
The fact that materials produced by other publishers may be referred to in this volume does not constitute an endorsement of the content or theological position of materials produced by such publishers. Any references and ancillary materials are listed as an aid to the student or the teacher and in an attempt to maintain the accepted academic standards of the publishing industry.

READING 1D
A Day to Remember
Third Edition

Coordinating Authors Susan J. Lehman Linda O. Parker	**Designers** David Siglin	**Composition** Carol Larson
Editor Debbie L. Parker	**Cover** Elly Kalagayan	**Photo Acquisition** Joyce Landis Carla Thomas
Project Manager Victor Ludlum		

Acknowledgments and photo credits are listed on page 127.

© 2005 BJU Press
Greenville, South Carolina 29609
First Edition © 1981 BJU Press
Second Edition © 1989 BJU Press

ISBN 978-1-59166-270-9
ISBN 978-1-59166-455-0 (READING 1A–1F Set)

15   14   13

Contents

A Day to Remember

Nobody Listens to Andrew 1
From the book, Nobody Listens to Andrew,
by Elizabeth Guilfoile

Kate's Blue Dress 16
Christian fiction by Charlene Killian

One Thing at a Time 25
A folktale
Adapted by Jan Joss

Let's Play School 32
Realistic fiction by Milly Howard

Something Sweet 36
Fanciful fiction by Gail Fitzgerald

A Special Welcome 41
Realistic fiction by Eileen M. Berry

A Day of Joy 50
Christian fiction based on a true story
by Gail Fitzgerald

A Ride to Remember 53
Humorous historical fiction by Libby Jumper

A Visit to the Dentist 62
Fanciful fiction by Elaine Johnson

Attack on Boone's Fort 70
Historical fiction by Libby Jumper

A Spring Surprise 78
Realistic fiction by Dottie Oberholzer

Brooms 86
Poetry by Dorothy Aldis

A Very Rainy Day 88
An essay by Milly Howard

The Contest on the Mountain 93
Taken from I Kings 18
Retold by Gail Fitzgerald

Ice the Cake 99
Fanciful fiction by Jamie Turner

The Gingerbread Boy 108
A folktale
Retold as a play by Janet Snow

Gingerbread Cookie Mix Gift Jar 118
A recipe

Yoshiko's Choice 120
A true missionary story by Gail Fitzgerald

Glossary 129

Nobody Listens to Andrew

From the book, Nobody Listens to Andrew
Elizabeth Guilfoile
illustrated by Jim Hargis

Too Busy

Andrew saw something upstairs.
He ran down very fast.
He said,
  "Listen, Mother."

Mother said,
"Wait, Andrew.
I must pay Mrs. Cleaner.
She must catch the bus before dark."

Andrew said,
    "Listen, Daddy.
    I saw something upstairs."
Daddy said,
    "Wait, Andrew.
    I must cut the grass before dark."

Andrew said,
    "Listen, Ruthy.
    I saw something upstairs.
    It was in my bed."
Ruthy said,
    "Wait, Andrew.
    I must put on my roller skates.
    I want to skate before dark."

Andrew said,

    "Listen, Bobby.

    I saw something upstairs.

    It was in my bed on the sun porch."

Bobby said,

    "Don't bother me, Andrew.

    I must find my bat and ball.

    I want to play ball before dark."

Andrew said,

"Listen, Mr. Neighbor.
I saw something upstairs.
It was in my bed on the sun porch.
It was black."

Mr. Neighbor said,

"Never mind, Andrew.
I must take my dog for a walk
before dark."

Andrew said very loud,
      "Listen, Mother,
      Listen, Daddy,
      Listen, Ruthy,
      Listen, Bobby,
      Listen, Mr. Neighbor,
      Listen, Mrs. Cleaner,
      THERE IS A BEAR UPSTAIRS
      IN MY BED."

Upstairs

Mother stopped paying Mrs. Cleaner.
    She said, "Call the police!"
Daddy stopped cutting the grass.
    He said, "Call the fire department!"
Bobby stopped playing ball.
    He said, "Call the dogcatcher!"
Ruthy stopped skating. She said,
    "Call the zoo!"

Mr. Neighbor stopped taking his dog for a walk.

He called the police.
He called the fire department.
He called the dogcatcher.
He called the zoo.

"Zoom!" came the police.
"Zing!" came the fire department.
"Whoosh!" came the dogcatcher.
"Swish!" came the man from the zoo.
They all ran upstairs.

"Look!" said Mother.

"It is on the sun porch."

"Look!" said Daddy. "It is black."

"Look!" said Bobby. "It is on Andrew's bed."

"Look!" said Ruthy.

"It is a bear.

Andrew said it was a bear.

But nobody listens to Andrew."

11

The dogcatcher caught the bear in his net.
The fireman said,
      "It climbed up the tree.
      It climbed in the window."

The man from the zoo said,
   "It is dry in the woods.
   The bears are thirsty.
   They are looking for water.
   I will take this bear to the zoo."
Daddy said . . .

"Next time we will listen to Andrew."

Who Said It?

Draw a line to match each person
with what he said in the story.

"It is in my bed!"

"I must cut the grass."

"I want to skate."

"I must pay Mrs. Cleaner."

Kate's Blue Dress

Charlene Killian
illustrated by Lynda Slattery

A Dress for Sunday

"What do you think of the dress Grandmother sent Kate?" Mom held the dress for Dad to see.

"It's pretty," said Dad. "It is just the color of Kate's eyes."

Kate giggled. "My eyes are not blue. They are brown."

"Well, so they are. We can give the dress to Grace. Grace has blue eyes," Dad teased.

"Dad is teasing," Mom said to Kate. "This dress is for Sunday."

"It's so pretty!" Kate said. "I love it."

"Grandmother will be glad you like it, Kate," Mom said. She put the dress on Kate's bed.

Kate leaned on the bed to see it better. "Will it fit?" she asked.

"I think so," said Mom. "I have to go get some things for supper. Do you want to come with me? When we get back, you can try the dress on."

Kate did not go with Mom. She went to the bed and picked up the dress. "It is a nice dress," she thought. "This dress will not be hard to put on. I do not need anyone's help. I can do it myself."

Kate put the dress on. The dress fit Kate just right. She tied the belt in the front. Kate spun and spun. She spun until she was dizzy.

"I will keep the dress on until Mom comes back," she thought. "She will see that it fits."

But Mom did not come back right away. Kate waited and waited. At last she went to the window. The grass in the front yard was cut, and Dad had gone to work in the back.

The cut grass smelled clean and sweet. Kate puffed up the sleeves of the pretty blue dress. She went to the door. She did not see Dad. She did not see Mom.

"I will go play in the front yard," Kate said. "I will wait for Mom there. I will have fun, and I will keep the dress clean. And I will see the car when it comes."

What Will Kate Do?

Kate went to play in the front yard. She ran on the fresh-smelling grass. She skipped and hopped in the sunshine. She darted under the branches of the trees. Then she spun to run back into the sunshine.

A tug at the hem of the dress stopped Kate. A low-hanging branch had snagged the blue dress.

"My dress!" Kate said. "It's ripped! I don't want Mom to see this! What will I do?"

Just then Mom drove up the road. Kate ran back inside.

Kate slipped off the blue dress. She put the other dress back on. Then she went to the car to meet Mom.

Mom parked the car. "I had a hard time getting what I needed at the store," she said. "Since I am running late, you can try the dress on some other time, Kate."

That night Kate put the dress by the bed. She went to bed, but she could not sleep.

"I didn't do what Mom said," Kate thought. "And I didn't tell Mom that the dress is ripped."

Kate got up to pray. "Please forgive me, God," she prayed. "I did not obey."

Kate went to get Mom. "I put on the dress," Kate said. "Then I went out to play, and I ripped it."

Mom was not happy. "You didn't obey," she said. "That is a sin. But I am glad you came to tell me."

"I asked God to forgive me," Kate said. "Will you forgive me?"

Mom smiled. "Yes, I will. And the rip isn't bad. I can fix it. Your dress will be fixed for Sunday."

Kate went back to bed. This time she could rest.

If we confess our sins, he is faithful and just to forgive us our sins.
—1 John 1:9

Grandmother's Gift

Draw a smile if Kate was happy.
Draw a frown if Kate was sad.

_____ Grandmother sent Kate a dress.

_____ The blue dress snagged on a branch.

_____ Kate could not sleep.

_____ Mom will fix the dress.

One Thing at a Time

A folktale adapted by Jan Joss
illustrated by Tim Davis

Busy, Busy, Busy

Once upon a time there was a little old lady who thought she had more to do than she had time for. She kept the fire hot and baked the cakes. She cleaned the windows and made the cheese. She did many things at once.

When the little old man came home, he sat in his rocker by the fire. "I had a nice day," he said.

The little old lady said, "My day was not nice. I was busy, busy, busy! I did not have time to sit and rock!"

The little old man thought and thought. At last he said, "I will do your job. You can do my job."

The next day the little old lady left the cabin to do the little old man's job.

She began by hunting for the goat. She fixed the rope for the goat's neck. She placed the rope on a stake next to the garden.

Then the little old lady put a harness on the mule. When they got to the field, the mule just sat. It would not work. "I will wait to finish this job," said the little old lady.

The little old lady went to the forest to chop logs. She chopped and chopped. The ax got stuck in the tree. "I will wait to finish this job," she said.

Finish the Job

Next the little old lady went to feed the pigs. One big pig broke the fence. The little old lady chased the pig. The big pig ran through the garden gate. It ran through the corn. It ran through the beans. It ran through the beets.

The pig came close to the goat. The pig's teeth seemed big and sharp to the goat. The goat broke its rope and began to run. The goat ran. The pig ran. And the little old lady ran. They ran to the field where the mule was still sitting.

The goat's horns seemed big and sharp to the mule. The mule began to run. The goat ran. The pig ran. And the little old lady ran. They ran into the forest.

Then the mule ran past the ax that was stuck in the tree! The tree fell with a crack!

The mule stopped!

The goat stopped!

The pig stopped!

The little old lady stopped!

"It is time to go home," she moaned and groaned.

The little old man was rocking by the fire. The cabin was clean. The butter was made. The supper was on the table.

"You can do your job. I will do my job!" said the little old lady. "My day was not nice. I was busy, busy, busy. I need time to rock."

The little old man thought and thought. "Just do one thing at a time," he said to the little old lady. "Then you will not be busy, busy, busy. You will have a nice day."

The next day the little old man left the cabin to start doing his job, one thing at a time.

Who Does it?

Circle the person who usually
does each job.

Cleans the windows

Harnesses the mule

Feeds the pigs

Bakes the cakes

Chops the logs

Let's Play School

Milly Howard
illustrated by John Roberts

Mark went to the window. The rain fell faster and faster. Mark did not think it would ever stop.

Mark sighed. "What can we do?" he asked his dog, Frisky.

Frisky whined and wagged his tail. He trotted through the door and came back with a bone. He dropped the bone at Mark's feet.

"No, we can't play with that," Mark said. Then he smiled. "But we can play school."

Mark went to a box and got some sunglasses. He put the glasses on Frisky.

"There, Frisky," he said. "This will not be hard. You can be in my school. I will be the teacher. We will have a class here. I will teach you a Bible verse."

Frisky perked up. He barked and wagged his tail. The glasses slid off his nose.

"No, Frisky," Mark said. "You can't wag your tail. Sit here and be still!"

Frisky sat. His happy bark became a sad whine. But Mark did not see that Frisky was not happy. Mark was putting paper and crayons into a backpack.

"Here, Frisky," he said. "This is your school bag. I will put it on your back for you. Then you can come to my school."

Frisky let Mark strap the backpack on him. He let Mark put him at the table. But Frisky was not happy. Frisky did not want to be in school. Frisky wanted to play.

Frisky jerked away. The backpack flapped on his back as he ran through the door.

"Wait, Frisky!" Mark yelled. "It isn't time to play. It is still time for school!"

But Frisky did not wait. And Frisky did not come back. Mark had to go get Frisky and the backpack.

"Come on, Frisky," he said to his dog. "We will not play school. I can see that school is not for dogs."

Frisky wagged his tail.

"But if we can't play school, maybe we can play store," Mark said. He picked up a can of beans. "I will be the clerk . . . "

Frisky backed away. In a flash, he was through the door and gone.

Something Sweet

Gail Fitzgerald
illustrated by Del Thompson

"Come," said Mother to the cub. "It is time to hunt something to eat. You must obey me. Stay close to me."

Mother and the cub left the den. Mother began to hunt for something to eat. She turned a big stone over. Grubs went everywhere.

"Eat!" said Mother as she ate.

"I will try it," said the cub to himself. He tumbled a stone over. It fell on him, and the grubs got away.

"Next time tumble the stone away from you," said Mother.

On they went up the hill. Mother sniffed the breeze.

"I smell a treat," said Mother. "I smell a bee tree. It will have something sweet to eat."

"What is sweet?" asked the cub.

Mother smiled and said, "You will see. Stay close to me."

Mother turned away. The cub trotted on. He hunted here and there for something sweet.

The cub came to a big stump. There was something black and white next to the stump.

"See, Mother!" yelled the cub. "Is this something sweet?"

"That isn't sweet. It is a skunk," she said. "It will make your fur smell bad. Stay away from skunks and stay close to me."

Mother went on, but the cub didn't. Next to a tree the cub came upon some chains.

"Mother!" yelled the cub. "Is this something sweet?"

Mother came running. "This trap will hurt you. It will snap shut on your feet," Mother said. "I see I have much to teach you."

Mother and the cub went on. At the curve of the hill, they came to a tree. Bees buzzed in the tree. A bee buzzed the cub, but the cub did not chase the bee. He stayed close to Mother.

"Up there is something sweet," said Mother.

Mother scrambled up the tree. The cub could hear her slurp as she ate.

The cub sat on the grass. "I can't get up the tree," he whimpered.

Drip, drip, drip. Something dropped on the end of his nose. He licked his nose.

"Is this something sweet?" he asked.

"Yes." His mother smiled. "This is something sweet."

A Special Welcome

Eileen M. Berry
illustrated by Keith Neely

Waiting for the Baby

Papá bent over Marta's bed. "Mamá and I are going, sleepy girl," he said. "But Abuela is here. Be a big girl and help her as much as you can."

Marta sat up so fast that her bed seemed to spin. "Going? To have the baby?" she asked.

Even in the dark, she thought Papá was smiling. "Yes," he said. "We are going to the hospital. It's time for the baby."

Marta rubbed her eyes. "Is it time to get up?"

Papá patted her hand. "No, go back to sleep," he said. "It will be a while. When the baby is born, you can come to the hospital."

Marta could not go back to sleep. "The day I have waited for is here!" she thought.

When Marta heard Grandma clattering pans, she leaped up from her bed. She ran to Grandma. "Abuela, the big day is here!" she said. "The baby will be born today!"

Grandma hugged her. "Yes, Marta. But not yet. Let's set the table."

"Do we have to go to school?" Carlos asked. "I can't sit still today. I feel like running and jumping!"

Grandma laughed. "Your Mamá said you could stay home today," she said. The children clapped.

"Play with me!" said Susita.

"Yes, there will be time for play," said Grandma. "But Carlos and Marta have to do some work."

"We want to help," said Carlos. "What can we do?"

"First," said Grandma, "you can eat some eggs and toast. After you get dressed, we will get to work."

After they ate, Marta and Carlos helped clean up the table. Then they got dressed.

Grandma handed Marta a rag. "Would you dust, please?" she asked. "We want the baby's things to be clean."

"Yes, I will dust," said Marta.

She went over to the baby's crib. "This is a nice place for a baby," she said to herself. "It is sunny and quiet. I think the baby will like it here." She dusted the crib well. Then she dusted the dresser and the rocker. She dusted under the window. Everything seemed to shine.

Marta started to tell Grandma the work was done. Then she thought of one more thing. She ran over to her own dresser and picked up her stuffed bunny, Muff. She ran her hand over the silky fur. Muff had been hers since she was a baby.

Marta put the bunny back on her dresser. Then she thought for a while. The baby might like to cuddle that silky fur. She picked up Muff and ran to the baby's crib. She set Muff in the crib.

Meeting the Baby

The phone rang. Marta heard Grandma say, "Thank the Lord! I am so glad."

Marta smiled at Carlos. Carlos grabbed Susita's hand. They ran to Grandma. "Is the baby born?" asked Carlos.

Grandma held the phone so they could hear. "Marta? Carlos? Susita? You have a little brother named Pedro," Papá said over the phone. "Mamá and baby are fine."

Susita clapped her hands. Carlos hopped. Marta smiled.

"When can we see him?" asked Marta.

"Abuelo and Abuela will bring you after supper," said Papá.

It was hard to wait! Marta and Carlos could not eat much supper.

Susita made up a tune. "Baby is here, Baby is here," she sang.

At last Grandpa drove them to the hospital.

Mamá was sitting up in bed. She held a little bundle in a blue blanket. "Pedro is sleeping," she said. "Would you like to peek?"

Marta, Carlos, and Susita gazed at the tiny face. "Hi, little brother," said Marta.

The baby wiggled and lifted his hand a little. "I think he's waving at us!" said Carlos.

Mamá and Papá laughed.

"He's opening his eyes!" said Grandma. "I think he's waking up."

"Mamá, will you put Pedro in my arms?" asked Marta.

Mamá smiled. "Yes. Sit here in the rocker," she said.

Marta held the blue bundle. "Pedro, I want to tell you some things," she said. "You have some nice things waiting for you at home. You have a sunny window and a clean crib. You have a nice mamá and papá. You have a sweet abuela and abuelo. You have two sisters named Marta and Susita. You have a big brother named Carlos. And you have a bunny named Muff."

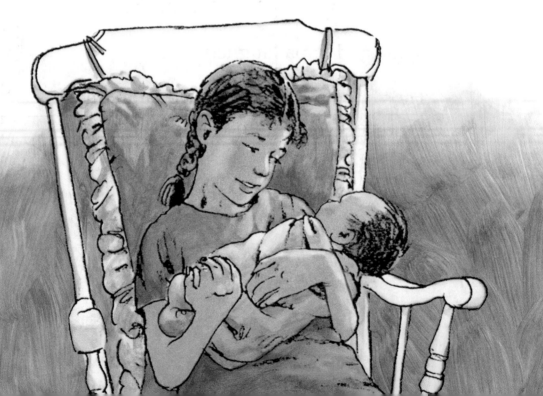

"But Marta, Muff is your bunny," said Mamá.

"No," said Marta. "I gave him to Pedro. He will need him more than I do."

Mamá put her hand on Marta's. "That was sweet of you," she said. "I think Pedro will like Muff."

"Pedro has a little smile on his face," said Carlos. "See? He is thinking of Muff."

Marta giggled. "Pedro likes his gift," she said.

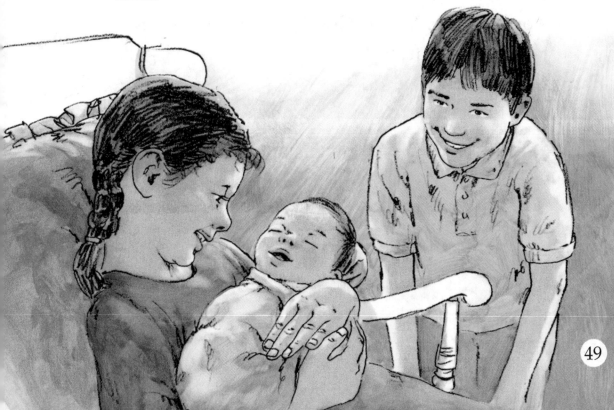

A Day of Joy

Gail Fitzgerald

"The storm is still coming. We have turned away from it two times. In a short time there will be nowhere to go," said Mr. York.

"We will ask God to show us a place to land the plane," Mr. Garland said.

"There is a lake. We can land on it," Mr. York said.

"I see some people on the shore," said Mr. Garland. "We will wait with them until the storm is over. Maybe God has someone for us to speak to of Jesus."

Mr. Garland landed the plane on the frozen lake. The men left the plane and went to meet the people.

A man led Mr. Garland and Mr. York to his home. Inside, a lady sat in the dim light of a little fire. The lady had no need of light, for she could not see. She sat by the fire to keep warm.

"May we come in?" Mr. York asked.

Mr. Garland said, "We have come to tell you of Jesus."

The lady clapped her hands. "Come in, come in," she said. "Please sit. I am so glad you came!"

The lady had a story for the men. "One day, when I was just twelve, some people came here. They spoke to us of Jesus. Then they left. That was many, many years ago. Since then I have prayed and prayed that someone would come and tell me more of Jesus."

That day the men led her to Jesus. The lady had much joy, the men had much joy, and heaven had much joy.

Joy shall be in heaven over one sinner that repenteth. —Luke 15:7

A Ride to Remember

Libby Jumper
illustrated by Del Thompson

Tin Lizzie

It was a fine day to go for a ride. Father cranked up Tin Lizzie and jumped in.

"Here we go!" said Father.

Tin Lizzie shot away like a frisky horse. Mother grabbed her hat. Henry turned back to see Tin Lizzie kicking up dust.

Tin Lizzie started up a hill. She chugged past some men who were digging at the side of the road. She chugged past a dog that was chasing a stick. She did not chug far. It was a big hill! Tin Lizzie chugged one more time, and then stopped. She started to roll back.

She rolled past the dog that was chasing the stick. She rolled past the men who were digging at the side of the road. The men liked to joke.

"Get a horse!" they yelled. "A horse does not roll."

Tin Lizzie just went on rolling back. When she came to the flat road, she stopped.

Father held the wheel and thought. The men were still yelling. Henry pulled his cap on tighter. The hill was still there.

"What will you do?" said Mother to Father.

"There is only one thing to do," said Father. "I will back her up the hill."

So he did.

He turned Tin Lizzie to face the road again. She went on for many miles. She zipped past homes. She zipped past gardens. She zipped past some children playing.

"This is more like it," said Father.

Bang! Flap, flap, flap.

"What is that?" Mother asked.

"The back tire has gone flat," said Father.

Flap, flap, flap went the tire. *Bump, bump, bump* went Henry.

The children who had been playing ran up.

"Get a horse!" they yelled. "A horse does not go flat."

Henry's face got very pink. "I would like to stop bumping," he mumbled.

Father stopped Tin Lizzie.

"What will you do?" asked Mother.

"There is only one thing to do," said Father. "I will fix the tire."

So he did.

Get a Horse

"We will get on with the drive," said Father.

Then it started to rain. *Splash!* A raindrop hit Henry on the arm.

"It is raining. We will get soaked," said Mother. "What will you do?"

"There is only one thing to do. I will put up the top," said Father.

So he did.

More rain came. The road got wet. Tin Lizzie splashed through the puddles. Her tires swished in the mud.

"This is fun!" said Henry.

The rain stopped. Tin Lizzie did not stop. Tin Lizzie slid. Her tires churned up the mud. Tin Lizzie came to a stop.

Tin Lizzie just sat. Father sat. Mother sat. Henry sat.

A man on a cart yelled, "Get a horse! A horse does not get stuck!"

And the man on the cart went on.

Mother turned to Father. Henry turned to Father.

"What will you do?" asked Mother.

Father thought and thought. "There is only one thing to do. I will have to push," he said.

Father bent to push. One shoe slipped. The other shoe slipped. Father fell flat in the mud.

Mother giggled. Henry giggled.

"What will you do?" asked Mother.

"There is only one thing to do. I will get a horse," said Father.

So he did.

Busy with Lizzie

Color the bubble next to each sentence that is true.

○ Tin Lizzie had to be cranked up.

○ Tin Lizzie played music.

○ Tin Lizzie had a flat tire.

○ Tin Lizzie was a bike.

○ Tin Lizzie got stuck in the mud.

A Visit to the Dentist

Elaine Johnson
illustrated by Cory Godbey

A Checkup

"After you finish your lunch, you must brush your teeth and put on your shoes," said Mrs. Beaver. "We are going to the dentist to get your teeth checked."

"What does a dentist do?" asked Betsy Beaver.

"Will it hurt?" asked Benny Beaver.

"The dentist will check your teeth with a little pick, and he will clean your teeth with paste and a brush that buzzes," said Mom. "I don't think it will hurt."

When Benny and Betsy got to the dentist, Miss Birdie was perched at the desk. She chirped a greeting to them, then fluttered through the papers on her desk.

A turtle in the lobby gazed at the beavers with eyes as big as eggs. "My name is Dozer. I just love waiting, don't you?" he said with a slow drawl. Then he went back to his reading.

At last Miss Birdie sent them in to see Dr. Brown.

Dr. Brown showed the beavers some of the things he would use to check their teeth. Then he gave each of them a little red tablet. "Crunch this up with your teeth," he said. "Then spit it into the sink."

They did just as Dr. Brown said. They were surprised to see little red spots on their teeth.

"Those stains are where your teeth did not get brushed well. A cavity could grow there. It is time for me to clean your teeth. Benny, would you like to sit in my big blue seat first?"

But Benny did not want to sit in the blue seat. *What if it hurts when the dentist cleans my teeth?* he thought.

Something to Keep

Benny gripped the seat as it went up, up, up.
Dr. Brown checked Benny's teeth with a little
pick. It did not hurt a bit! Then Dr. Brown
cleaned Benny's teeth. The buzzing brush
tickled a little bit, but it did not hurt.

After Dr. Brown cleaned Benny's teeth, he
checked and cleaned Betsy's too.

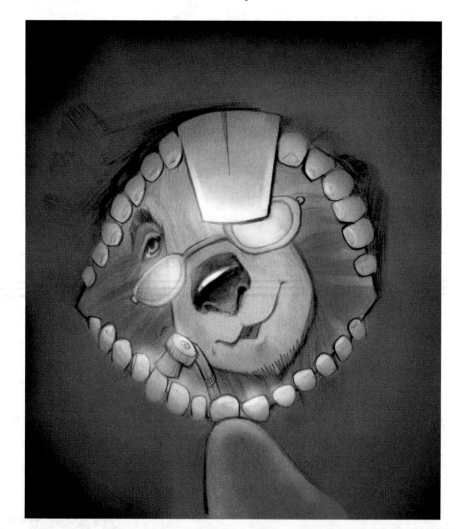

"You can hop off the seat, Betsy," said Dr. Brown. Then he gave each of them a toothbrush and a little tube of toothpaste.

"Are these for us to take home?" asked Betsy.

Dr. Brown nodded. "You two are brushing your teeth well. I did not see one cavity. When you get home, throw away the brush you have been using. Then start brushing with this brush. Keep brushing after each meal and eat things that are best for beaver teeth."

"What things are best for beaver teeth?" asked Betsy.

Dr Brown smiled. "Apples, leaves, bark, and fish will help beaver teeth. And sticks will sharpen your teeth."

Dr. Brown led them back to the desk where Miss Birdie kept a pretty basket. "I have something here for you," she said. "You may get one thing from this basket. It is full of fun things."

Benny reached inside the basket and chose a little sailboat. Then Betsy chose a pretty butterfly ring.

Just then, Benny spotted Dozer in the corner of the lobby. He was hiding in his shell. A muffled voice came from the shell. "Did it hurt?" the voice drawled.

"No!" Benny exclaimed. "It was fun!"

Dozer popped his head up from his shell and grinned as Miss Birdie tweeted, "Dozer Turtle, you're next!"

Attack on Boone's Fort

Libby Jumper
illustrated by Preston Gravely Jr.

Two Tunnels

It was quiet. The fighting had stopped. What was going on?

From the top of the stockade, Daniel Boone could see the river. Something was not right.

Just past the fort, Daniel could see muddy water in the river. Someone was throwing dirt into the river. Where was the dirt coming from?

Daniel went up higher to see better. He did not like what he was seeing.

The Indians were digging a tunnel from the riverbank to the fort.

"What will we do?" asked Daniel's men.

"We will dig a tunnel too," said Daniel. "It will run under the cabins by the stockade. The Indian tunnel will have to run into it. Maybe we can stop them there."

Daniel's men got busy on their tunnel, but the fighting started up again. Some men were digging, while other men were fighting. They worked day and night.

Sometimes the Indians attacked at night. Sometimes they crept up to the fort and shot burning arrows into the fort.

71

The men did not have a lot of water. They needed to save what water they had for drinking. So they beat the flames with blankets. But arrows were blazing everywhere. The flames went from roof to roof. The fort was on fire!

Daniel and his men prayed. Then it began to rain. The fire sputtered. The flames began to flicker and die. The happy men gave thanks to God.

It rained through the night. It rained through the next day.

Daniel went to check on the tunnel. The men had stopped digging.

"Quiet!" Daniel whispered.

Daniel waited in the tunnel. Daniel stood still. The men waited. They listened.

Chink! Chink!

Someone was digging.

The Storm

"The Indians are close," Daniel said. "They might dig through at any moment."

The men left the tunnel and ran back into the fort. They waited, but the Indians did not attack.

That night rain gave way to a real storm. The wind tore at the rooftops. The rain fell in sheets. The thunder rumbled and crashed. Lightning flashed in the sky.

Daniel's men were afraid. They could not see or hear over the storm. Would the Indians come through the tunnel in the storm? Would Daniel's men see them in time? Would they be able to stop the Indians?

The men were brave. They would put up a good fight. But could thirty men stop hundreds of Indians?

It stormed through the night. Daniel and his men huddled next to the stockade fence. The freezing rain whipped their faces.

Daniel and his men had been glad for the rain at first. But this storm seemed to be helping the Indians.

The men prayed for the morning to come. Just before it was time for the sun to rise, the storm stopped. Everything was still. No arrows shot into the sky. There was no attack on the fort.

"Where are the Indians?" Daniel asked.

"Maybe they gave up," said one of the men.

"But why?" asked Daniel.

There was a yell from a man on top of the stockade. "Look! Look at the Indian tunnel!"

More men went up to look. They began to yell.

What a sight! The rain had soaked the dirt. The tunnel had caved in. The Indians were gone. The men were safe.

A Spring Surprise

Dottie Oberholzer
illustrated by Keith Neely

The Hike

Alex scrambled up the hill. The fresh breeze was in his face. He loved exploring the trails. The snow was gone, and the sun was warm. He was excited to be on a hike. There were many things to see in the woods.

Alex stopped to pick up a twig to throw for Buddy while the rest of the family made it up the hill.

"I have a plan," said Dad. "Let's hunt for clues that spring is here. Let's see who can spot one."

Alex liked Dad's plan. "That will be fun!" he said.

"I see some buds!" said Ashley. Under a pile of brown leaves, little purple buds were peeking through.

"Over here!" said Mom. "Here are some pretty buttercups."

They spotted a bird with a twig hanging from its beak. "This is another clue of spring," said Dad. "The birds are making their nests. They will soon be laying their eggs."

"Could we make a birdhouse so the birds will make a nest in the yard?" asked Alex.

"That's a great plan," said Dad. "Let's go home and get started."

Dad cut the boards. Alex hammered in the nails. At last, the birdhouse was done.

Days passed, and Alex kept waiting for some clue that a bird was making a nest in the birdhouse. Birds went past the birdhouse. But he did not see any birds land on the perch. And he did not see any birds fly into the tiny hole.

"Why don't the birds like the home we made them?" asked Alex.

"Maybe they will live in it next spring. Don't give up hope," said Dad.

But Alex felt sad that the birds did not want to make a home in his yard.

The Surprise

One evening Mom said, "Let's have a picnic supper and grill hot dogs. We can even eat on the porch."

"Can we help you, Mom?" asked Ashley.

"Here, put ice in the cups, Ashley," said Mom. "And, Alex, you can help your dad clean the grill. We have not used it since last summer."

Alex went to get Dad. He was hunting for the wire brush to clean the grill. "I am here to help," said Alex.

"Thanks," said Dad.

Alex and Dad went to the grill with the brush. Alex opened the lid of the grill and gasped at what was inside.

A mother bird had made a nest in the corner of the grill! Tucked inside the nest were five tiny white eggs with brown flecks.

"Come and see what is in the grill!" Alex yelled. Mom and Ashley and Buddy came running.

"What a surprise!" said Mom. "A mother bird has been at work here."

"Where does she get inside the grill?" asked Alex. He was keeping Buddy back from the nest.

"Let's wait for the mother bird to come back. Then we will see," said Mom.

"We will have to make supper another way," Dad said.

While they waited for the mother bird, Dad made a campfire.

Dad put hot dogs on a stick. Then he held the stick over the fire. They sat on the porch to eat.

"The mother bird just went into the grill!" Mom whispered. "And there she goes again!"

"I see why she likes the grill," said Ashley. "She has a front door and a back door!"

Dad smiled at Alex. "A bird did want to make a home right here in the yard, didn't she?"

Alex felt happy. He loved the spring surprise.

Full Flight

Read the story.

   "Alex and Ashley, come and see!" said Mom. They rushed to the window where Mom was standing.

   "What is it?" asked the twins.

   "The mother bird is teaching the little birds to fly," said Mom.

Color the bubble next to the sentence that tells what will happen next.

O The birds will swim.
O The kittens will learn to walk.
O The birds will fly.

Brooms

Dorothy Aldis
illustrated by Preston Gravely Jr.

On stormy days
When the wind is high
Tall trees are brooms
Sweeping the sky.
They swish their branches
In buckets of rain,
And swash and sweep it
Blue again.

A VERY RAINY DAY

Milly Howard

illustrated by Stephanie True

In my home, we have a box. It is a special box. Mom keeps it in a chest up in her room. And there it stays waiting for a Very Rainy Day.

A Very Rainy Day can't be a rainy day that comes and goes without much to say for itself. It has to be a foggy rain that mists up the windows. It has to be a drippy rain that puddles up the yard.

On days like that Mom brings down the box. Sometimes the box has things to play with in it. Sometimes they are things we have not seen for a while. Sometimes they are things we have never seen before.

Sometimes the box has lots of things to make music. There will be sand blocks and drums and flutes. There will be pot lids and hammers and jingle bells. It is hard to choose, but we do. Then we march from room to room. Mom and Dad do not fuss or frown, but sometimes I think they put cotton in their ears.

Sometimes the box has things to do in it. There will be books on how to make things. There will be empty boxes that Mom has saved so we can play store. I like being the store clerk. I add up the things people buy. I can add up the money and then put stuff in bags.

Sometimes the box has lots of dresses and shirts and hats in it. We dress up. I can be a lady in high-heeled shoes. We can put on a circus for Mom and Dad. In a circus, I can put on a pretty gown and ride a fine horse or make people laugh when I act like a clown. I can be anything I want to be, just for a little while.

So when the sky is not blue, I think of the box. When raincoats drip and boots splash, I think of the box. When books are damp and papers are limp, I think of the box. And when Mom brings down the box from her room, it must be a Very Rainy Day indeed!

Play Day

Draw a line from each playtime activity to its matching box of items.

To play dress-up

sand blocks   drums
jingle bells   flutes
pot lids

To make music

empty boxes
bags
play money

To play store

dresses
shirts
hats
rings
shoes

The Contest on the Mountain

Taken from 1 Kings 18
Gail Fitzgerald

Two Altars

King Ahab pounded his fist on the table. He shouted at God's man, Elijah. "You are bringing much harm to my people. Their cattle die. Their crops die. There is no water to drink."

Elijah gave the king God's answer. "You have not obeyed the true God. You are the reason that there is no rain. You seek after the god Baal. Bring your people to Mount Carmel. We will have a contest to see who is the true God."

So Ahab had his people come up to the top of the mountain. Elijah said, "We will make two altars. Each of us will make an offering. The true God will send fire."

Elijah stood off by himself. But he did not feel alone. God was with him.

Ahab's men made an altar to Baal. They began to pray. They asked their god to send fire on their altar. They prayed from morning until noon.

Elijah spoke to Ahab's men. "Pray harder," he said.

Ahab's men prayed harder. They raced back and forth in front of the altar. They shouted out loud.

Still their god did not answer.

"Try once more. Maybe Baal is sleeping," Elijah mocked. "Maybe your god is playing or taking a trip. What good is a god who cannot be found?"

The men prayed on from noon to night, jumping and leaping in front of the altar.

Still the fire did not come. The god of Ahab did not send fire.

One God

Ahab paced back and forth. There was not one thing that he could do. Elijah had to be given his turn.

Elijah took twelve very big stones. He set them in place to make an altar. Then he dug a trench around the altar.

"Fill four barrels with water. Put the water on the altar," Elijah said to the people. They obeyed Elijah.

"Do it again," Elijah said. They did it again.

"Do it a third time," Elijah ordered. They did it a third time. By this time the ground was muddy. Water filled the trench around the altar.

Elijah did not jump and race in front of the altar.

Elijah bowed and prayed to his God. "Lord, You are the true God," he prayed. "You can do anything. Please show these people that You are God."

Then the fire of the Lord fell! It burned up
the offering. It licked up the water in the
trench. It burned up the twelve stones and the
wood. It scorched the garments of those who
stood too close to the altar.

The people fell on their faces. "The Lord,
he is God; The Lord, he is God," they said.
Now they too could see that Elijah's God
was the one true God.

Thou shalt have none other gods before me. —Deuteronomy 5:7

Ice the Cake

Jamie Turner
illustrated by Kathy Pflug

Tidbit's Birthday

Champ, Nipper, and Gus had to hurry home from school. They were going to babysit their little sister, Tidbit.

"Tidbit is sleeping," said Mother when they got home. "Give her a bottle of milk when she wakes up. And please put icing on Tidbit's cake while I am gone."

They looked into the bowl at the creamy pink icing. "That will be fun!" they shouted.

"Dad is outside working in the yard if you need help," said Mother. She put on her coat and went out the door.

Nipper ran to the bowl of icing and grabbed it. "I want to be first!" he said.

Gus stomped his feet hard. "You never let me go first!" he said. "And I'm tired of it!" He yanked the bowl from Nipper.

"Wait!" said Champ. "You haven't washed your hands yet." Champ took the bowl from Gus and set it back on the table.

Nipper and Gus raced to the sink. They pushed each other and splashed the water. They didn't even take time to dry their hands. They ran back to the table.

Gus reached the bowl first this time and grabbed it with his slippery hands. "I will show you how to swirl the icing to make it pretty," he said.

"No, let me do it!" whined Nipper, tugging at the bowl. "I had it first!"

"Stop!" said Champ. "You two are dripping water into the icing."

Just then they heard a shrill cry from Tidbit. Champ set the bowl back on the table. "I will try to rock Tidbit back to sleep," he said. "Then we will take turns with the icing. Maybe you two should dry your hands while I'm gone."

When Champ left, Gus stormed off to dry his hands.

But Nipper just wiped his hands on his shirt. Then he picked up the bowl again and stirred the icing.

"This is easy," said Nipper. He put just a little bit on the top of the cake and twirled it into a creamy peak. It was like a little pink curl.

When Gus came back, he was upset. "You didn't wait for me to help!" he said. And he jerked the bowl from Nipper's hands. Nipper and Gus tugged back and forth on the bowl, then . . . CLANG! The bowl fell to the floor.

"What was that?" Champ yelled. He ran in with Tidbit, who was still whimpering. On the floor lay a giant puddle of pink icing.

Nipper and Gus gulped. What would Mother say when she came home? They had to do something–fast!

A Plan

Champ had a plan. He set Tidbit in her baby swing. "She can drink her bottle of milk while we clean up this mess."

The three chipmunks scraped the big globs of icing into the dustpan and dropped them into the trash bag. Then they mopped the floor.

"It is taking a lot more time to clean up our mess than it did to make it," said Gus as he scrubbed.

Tidbit drank her milk. She kicked her little legs and giggled with glee as her brothers were cleaning up their mess.

"At least one of us is having fun," said Nipper. He gave Tidbit a gentle pat.

103

Champ said to his brothers, "I need your help to make more icing. I've seen Mother do it many times. But this time we can't act selfish. We have to work as a team."

Gus and Nipper nodded.

Gus got the butter, and Nipper got the milk. The three of them got the big sugar jar from the top shelf. Then they whipped up a bowl of creamy white icing.

"There!" said Champ. "We did it! It isn't pink like Mother's, but it tastes fine. This time let's take turns icing the cake." And they did.

The cake was very pretty with white swirls and whirls. Tidbit waved her little fists and gurgled. "Ga-ga-do-da-da-pitty!" Her brothers smiled.

Mother came home a little later. When she looked at the pretty birthday cake she was puzzled. The cake was white, not pink. She asked the chipmunks to sit with her in the rocker.

Champ, Nipper, and Gus scrambled into her lap. "How did that icing get from pink to white?" she asked them.

This time no one wanted to go first. At last Nipper spoke up. "I started it by being selfish," he said.

"And I acted just as bad," said Gus.

"I gave everybody orders," said Champ. "But in the end we worked together."

After they had taken turns explaining, Mother hugged them tight. "I'm glad you found out that WE makes a better team than ME," she said.

Who's Who?

Write the number of the character to answer the questions.

1. Mother

2. Gus

3. Nipper
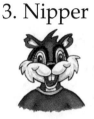

4. Champ

5. Tidbit

_____ Who dropped the bowl on the floor?

_____ Who drank milk?

_____ Who rocked the baby?

_____ Who said, "WE makes a better team than ME"?

The Gingerbread Boy

Retold as a play by Janet Snow
illustrated by Julie Speer

Cast

Narrator
Little old woman
Little old man
Gingerbread boy
Lazy black dog
Big brown horse
Fat pink pig
Sleek red fox

Casting Call Today!
The Gingerbread Boy Play

Act I

Narrator: Once upon a time, in a home not far from here, a little old woman was baking. Good sweet smells filled the house.

Little old woman: Now, let me see . . . flour, an egg, some sugar, and a pinch of spice. That will make you taste nice.

Narrator: She cut out a nice big gingerbread boy. Then she put him in the oven to bake.

Little old woman: (taking the pan out of the oven) Mmm! You smell so good. Here are two raisins for your eyes, and this orange gumdrop will be your hat.

Narrator: Then she used blue icing to dress him in a little blue coat. A curved line of white icing made his mouth, and a red heart made his cheek.

Little old woman: You will be a yummy treat for our supper.

Little old man: I can't wait for supper. I could eat the gingerbread boy right now!

Narrator: But the gingerbread boy did not want that. He gave a big leap, jumped from the pan, and ran out the door!

Little old woman: Come back! You must not run away. Oh my! There goes our supper.

Narrator: The gingerbread boy ran down the lane. Faster and faster he ran. The little old woman ran, and the little old man ran.

Little old man: Come back, come back. You are my supper.

Gingerbread boy: Away I go. This is fun. You can't catch me. I can run, run, run.

Narrator: And the gingerbread boy ran faster than the little old woman and the little old man. After a bit he passed a lazy black dog that was snoozing in the sun.

Lazy black dog: Woof! Woof! Gingerbread boy, slow down. Why are you in such a hurry?

Gingerbread boy: (laughing) I ran away from a little old woman and a little old man. And I can run away from you. I can, I can.

Lazy black dog: Maybe so, maybe not!

Go Gingerbread Boy!

Narrator: The gingerbread boy ran faster than the lazy dog, who forgot about being lazy.

Gingerbread boy: Away I go. This is fun. You can't catch me. I can run, run, run.

Narrator: And the gingerbread boy outran the lazy black dog. By the side of the road, a big brown horse grazed in the sun.

Big brown horse: Neigh, neigh! Come back here. You look so good to eat.

Gingerbread boy: No, no! I ran away from the little old woman and the little old man, and a lazy black dog. And I can run away from you. I can, I can!

Big brown horse: I don't think so. I can win a race, and I can get a gingerbread boy.

Narrator: The big brown horse joined the chase. The gingerbread boy laughed.

Gingerbread boy: Away I go. This is fun. You can't catch me. I can run, run, run.

Act II

Narrator: The big brown horse ran fast. But the gingerbread boy ran faster. They passed a fat pink pig eating corn by a barn.

Fat pink pig: Oink! Oink! Come back here, gingerbread boy. You look so good to eat. I could eat you in one big bite.

Gingerbread boy: No, no! I don't think so, fat pink pig. I ran away from a little old woman and a little old man, a lazy black dog and a big brown horse. I can run from you. I can, I can.

Fat pink pig: I don't think so! People think I'm slow, but you look sooooo good to eat. I will catch up with you.

Narrator: The fat pink pig puffed along after the gingerbread boy.

Gingerbread boy: Away I go. This is fun. You can't catch me. I can run, run, run.

Narrator: The gingerbread boy ran faster. The path wound through the woods. And it was there that the gingerbread boy heard from the sleek red fox.

Sleek red fox: What a pretty blue coat, what nice raisin eyes. I can just taste that orange gumdrop hat.

Gingerbread boy: Away I go. This is fun. You can't catch me. I can run, run, run.

Sleek red fox: Don't be so sure. Fox is my name.

Gingerbread boy: I ran away from the little old woman and a little old man, a lazy black dog, a big brown horse, a fat pink pig, and I can run from you. I can, I can!

Narrator: The sleek red fox ran after the gingerbread boy. But the fox had a sneaky plan. He had been down this path before. It led to a wide stream. Just then the gingerbread boy came to the stream.

Gingerbread boy: No, no! What will I do?

Sleek red fox: I will help you, gingerbread boy. Jump on my back. I will keep your pretty blue coat dry. I will help you swim to the other side.

Narrator: The gingerbread boy jumped onto the back of the sleek red fox. The fox began to swim.

Sleek red fox: Gingerbread boy, this is too hard. My back is going under the water. Jump up by my ear.

Narrator: The gingerbread boy did not want to get wet. He pulled himself up next to the ear of the fox.

Gingerbread boy: This is better. Thank you, fox.

Narrator: The fox swam slower and slower.

Sleek red fox: Gingerbread boy, my ears are going under the water. Jump up on my nose, so I can keep you out of the water.

Narrator: The gingerbread boy jumped up to the nose of the sleek red fox. Now he could see the other side of the stream.

Gingerbread boy: I ran away from a little old woman and a little old man, a lazy black dog, a big brown horse, and a fat pink pig. And I can run from you. I can, I can.

Narrator: The sleek red fox grinned. He was having fun. Then "Snap! Snap!" In two bites the gingerbread boy was gone!

Sleek red fox: The gingerbread boy, what became of him? He could run fast, but he could not swim.

Gingerbread Cookie Mix Gift Jar

Materials:
1-quart canning jar with lid
6-inch circle of fabric
12-inch length of ribbon

Ingredients:
2 cups all-purpose flour
1 teaspoon baking powder
1 teaspoon baking soda
1 cup packed brown sugar
1½ cups all-purpose flour
2 teaspoon ground ginger
1 teaspoon ground cloves
1 teaspoon ground cinnamon

1. First, mix 2 cups of flour with the baking powder and baking soda. Put the mixture into the jar to make the bottom layer of ingredients.

2. Next, put the brown sugar into the jar to make the middle layer of ingredients.

3. Finally, mix the additional 1½ cups of flour with the ginger, cloves, and cinnamon. Put the mixture into the jar to make the top layer.

4. Put the lid on the jar. Put the fabric on top of the lid. Tie the fabric onto the lid with the ribbon. Attach the recipe for *Gingerbread Cookies* to the jar.

Gingerbread Cookies

1. Empty the ingredients from the jar into a large mixing bowl. Stir the ingredients together.

2. Add:
   - ½ cup softened butter or margarine
   - ¾ cup molasses
   - 1 beaten egg

3. Stir ingredients together.

4. Cover and refrigerate for 1 hour or more.

5. Preheat oven to 350° F.

6. Roll dough to ½ inch thickness on floured surface.

7. Cut into shapes with cookie cutter.

8. Place cookies on greased cookie sheet.

9. Bake for 10-12 minutes.

10. Decorate with icing and candy.

Icing

Yoshiko's Choice

A true story
Gail Fitzgerald

Kendo

Yoshiko slipped off her shoes. Then she opened the quiet paper door. The tiny Japanese girl bowed to Grandmother before sitting on the mat floor. Mother was serving tea.

"Yoshiko, come and chat with me. Something is bothering you." Mother's quiet voice made Yoshiko feel better.

Yoshiko sighed. "My friend, Megumi, has gone on a fishing trip with her father. Today is not Bible club day. What can I do?"

"You are too shy," Mother said. "You need to make more friends. Father thinks it might help you to take kendo. Tomorrow you can begin."

After school the next day, Yoshiko started down the road. Her feet sped past the rice paddy. They went slower past the fishing boats. At last they stopped at the door of the kendo school. It was not too late to run home.

"Japanese people do not run away," said Yoshiko to herself. "It is not good to run away." She held her chin up and went in the door. Many children were dressed for their lessons. Yoshiko rushed to get dressed. She did not want to be different. She did not want people to look at her.

Class began. The children bowed first to the god shelf. Then they bowed to the teacher. He said it was good to bow to the god shelf. Those who did not bow would not do well at kendo.

After the first week, Yoshiko began to enjoy her kendo lessons. It was fun to shout and leap with her stick. Sometimes Yoshiko was the winner of the game. Sometimes she did not win. Sometimes the game was a tie.

The God Shelf

After school each Monday it was time for Bible club. Yoshiko enjoyed telling the Bible club teacher all about the kendo lessons. Yoshiko rushed down the road. She went past the rice paddy, past the fishing boats, past the kendo school, right to the Bible teacher's house. Miss Cochran seemed happy to hear what Yoshiko had to say.

And Yoshiko was eager to hear the Bible story each week. She had just become a Christian at Bible club. Now the Bible and kendo were more important to Yoshiko than anything.

One Monday Miss Cochran's Bible story was about some brave men. Yoshiko had not heard of them before. After club time she left right away. She wanted to be alone. She wanted to think about Daniel's three friends who would not bow before a false god. They were thrown into the fire!

Yoshiko took small slow steps past the
fishing boats. She went on past the rice paddy
to her home. Slipping off her shoes at the door,
Yoshiko entered her house. Mother was
putting pretty flowers on the table.

Mother saw Yoshiko's sad face. "Yoshiko, come sit by me. How can I help you?"

Yoshiko sighed. "I love my kendo classes. But my friends bow to the god shelf. Today at Bible club I heard about three friends who obeyed God. They did not bow to the false god. What can I do?"

"You must ask the Lord to show you," said Mother.

That night Yoshiko twisted and turned on her sleeping mat. She could not sleep. She had to make a choice.

"Daniel's friends were willing to be different," she said to herself. "It was more important to them to obey God than to live. I must obey God too. I will not bow to the god shelf anymore. Jesus is more important to me than kendo."

Peace filled Yoshiko's heart, and the restless feeling left her. She pulled up her blanket and went to sleep. It was a day she would always remember.

Acknowledgments

"Brooms," from EVERYTHING AND ANYTHING by Dorothy Aldis, copyright 1925–1927, renewed 1953, © 1954, 1955 by Dorothy Aldis. Used by permission of G.P. Putnam's Sons, A division of Penguin Young Readers Group, A Member of Penguin Group (USA) Inc., 345 Hudson St., New York, NY 10014. All rights reserved.

From *Nobody Listens to Andrew* by Elizabeth Guilfoile © 1957 by Pearson Education, Inc., publishing as Modern Curriculum Press, an imprint of Pearson Learning Group. Originally published by Follett Publishing Company. Used with permission.

Photo Credits

The following agencies and individuals have furnished materials to meet the photographic needs of this textbook. We wish to express our gratitude to them for their important contribution.

Corbis
James E. Gordon
Hemera Technologies
Joyce Landis

Susan Perry
PhotoDisc/Getty Images
Carla Thomas
www.arttoday.com

Glossary
© 2004 Hemera Technologies, Inc. All rights reserved. 129 (arrow, bucket), 134 (roller skates); **PhotoDisc/Getty Images** 129 (bear, birdhouse), 130 (bottom), 132 (top, bottom), 133 (old barn), 134 (storm clouds), 135 (bottom); **Joyce Landis** 130 (top), 135 (middle), 136; **James E. Gordon** 131 (top); © 2004 www.arttoday.com 131 (bottom); **Corbis** 133 (offering plate); **Carla Thomas** 134 (shoe), 135 (top); **Susan Perry** 134 (swirl)

Glossary

A

al·tar

Abraham offered a sacrifice on the altar.

ar·row

John shot the arrow with his bow.

B

bear

The furry black bear was eating honey.

bird·house

A bird lives in the birdhouse.

buck·et

I put the berries in the bucket.

C

car

A red car went down the road.

climb

John likes to climb trees.

curve

The mountain road had a big curve in it.

D

diz·zy

Spinning in circles makes me dizzy.

E

F

for·est

The forest has many kinds of trees.

fur

The kitten has soft fur.

G

gar·den

Grandpa plants beans and corn in his garden.

gin·ger·bread

Gingerbread tastes spicy.

H

har·ness

The farmer put the harness on the horse.

heav·en

Heaven has streets of pure gold.

hos·pi·tal

The doctor works at the hospital.

hurt

Bill hurt his knee on a rock.

I

J

Jap·a·nese

The Japanese girl wore a kimono.

K

ken·do

Bamboo swords are used in kendo.

L

limp

After the rain the flag was limp.

M

moun·tain

The men will climb the high mountain.

N

neigh

My horse will neigh when he is hungry.

O

of·fer·ing

I give money as an offering to the Lord.

old

The old barn is falling down.

P

perch

The bird sits on its perch.

po·lice

The police captured the bank robber.

pud·dle

The rain makes a puddle on the ground.

Q

R

rain·drop

A tiny raindrop hit the umbrella.

roll·er skates

Tim checked the wheels on his roller skates.

S

shoe

I can find only one shoe.

stock·ade

The soldiers were safe in the stockade.

storm·y

Dark clouds filled the stormy sky.

swirl

Kathy can swirl two colors together.

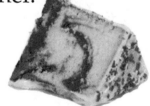

T

tab·let

Jason will draw a picture in his art tablet.

tooth·paste

Use toothpaste when you brush your teeth.

tore

Sam tore his shirt on a nail.

tube

The artist squeezed paint from the tube.

tur·tle

A turtle walks slowly.

U

V

W

whis·per

Let me whisper a secret in your ear.

Y

yard

Andy and Josh are playing in the back yard.

Z